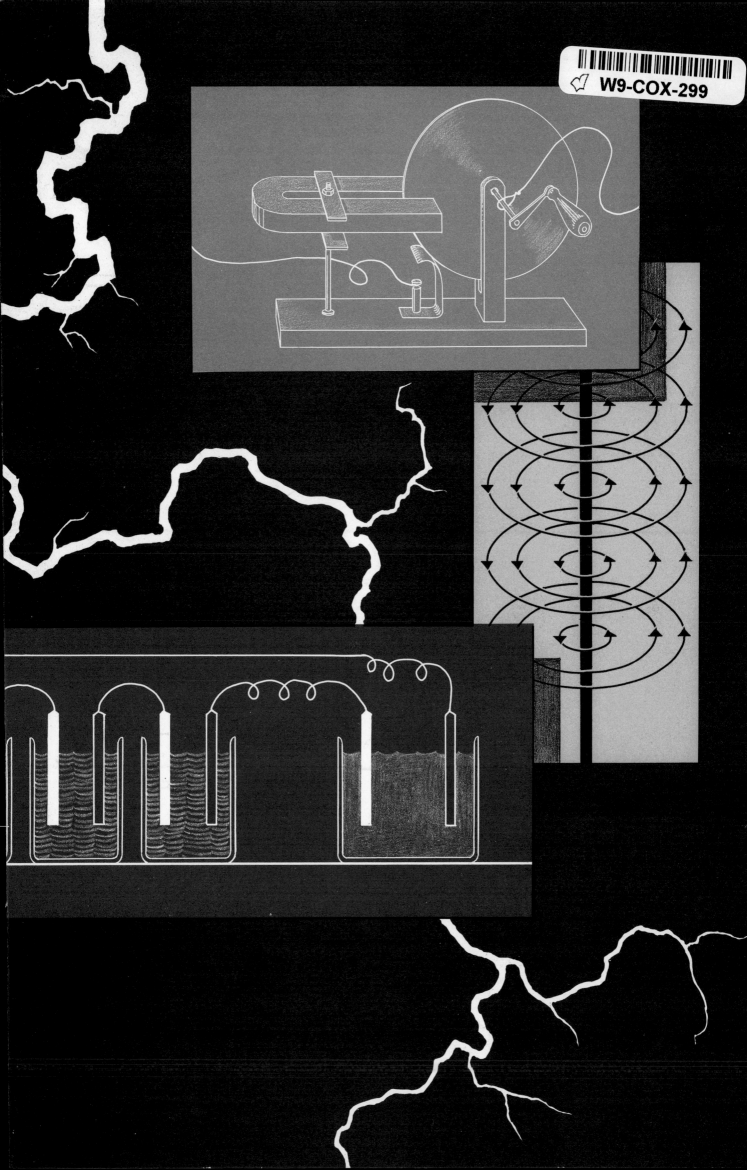

The Quest of Michael Faraday

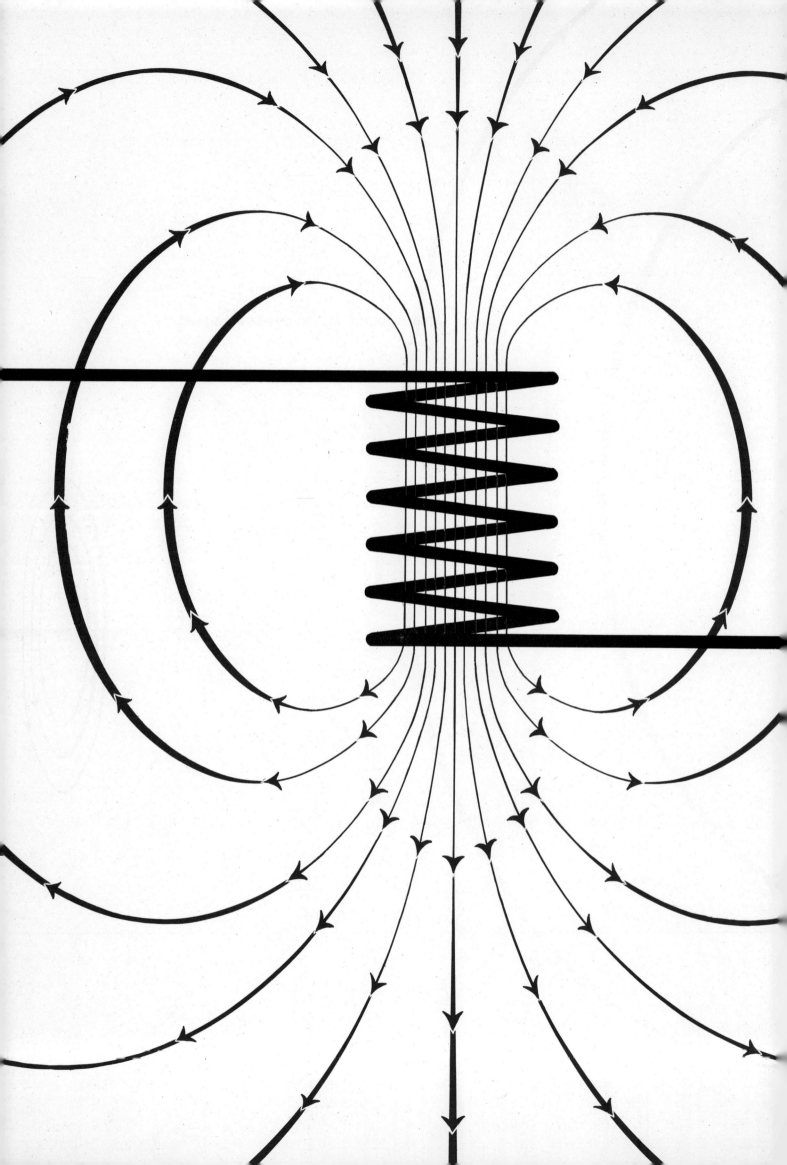

the quest of

Michael

Faraday

BY TAD HARVEY

ILLUSTRATED BY LEE J. AMES

GARDEN CITY BOOKS • GARDEN CITY, NEW YORK • 1961

Other Books in This Series

THE QUEST OF GALILEO
By Patricia Lauber

THE QUEST OF ISAAC NEWTON
By Barbara and Myrick Land

THE QUEST OF LOUIS PASTEUR
By Patricia Lauber

Acknowledgments

The author wishes to thank Dr. Robert E. Schofield, associate professor
of the History of Science, University of Kansas, for his valuable
criticism on the manuscript of this book; and Mrs. Adele Matthysse,
librarian of the Burndy Library, Norwalk, Connecticut, for making
available Burndy's fine collection of books by and about Faraday.

He is also in debt to Patricia Lauber, without whose help and encouragement
this book would not have been written in the first place.

Library of Congress Catalog Card Number 60-6176
Copyright © 1961 by Doubleday & Company, Inc.
All Rights Reserved
Printed in the United States of America
Designed by Alma Reese Cardi
First Edition

contents

An experimental philosopher

This is the story of a scientist who was also a philosopher, a philosopher who worked with magnets and wires, electric currents and chemicals. It is the story of a man who formed scientific theories in his mind, then tested their truth with his own hands, in experiments he himself had set up. This is Michael Faraday, who discovered how to change magnetism into electricity and thus gave us a way to generate the immense amounts of electrical power we use today. To this English scientist, more than any other single man, we owe our age of electricity.

Faraday himself would be quite surprised that we praise him now, less than a hundred years after his death, for making possible our wealth of electrical systems, electrical machines, devices, and appliances. In his lifetime, his electrical discoveries had very little practical value. It would surprise him, too, that we tend to link his name only with electrical power. For Faraday's interests, far from being specialized, reached out into almost every aspect of chemistry and physics.

Faraday was a philosopher in both name and temperament. Science in his time was considered a branch of philosophy. It was called "natural philosophy" because it dealt with the natural, not the supernatural, world: scientists were "natural philosophers."

Faraday was a philosopher in a deeper, more modern sense. Behind all his scientific research was a profound philosophical belief. This was a belief in the fundamental simplicity of the natural world. All of nature's workings, he felt, were governed by a few fixed and unchanging laws. For Faraday, the highest goal of the scientist was to discover and understand these laws. He dedicated his whole life to that quest.

6

Yet if Faraday was a true philosopher, he was also a great experimenter, perhaps one of the greatest in the history of science. Several of his discoveries were the result of doing a certain experiment a little more thoroughly, a little more alertly, than it had ever been done before.

Performing an experiment, he felt, was like submitting a question to nature. He was asking, "Is my theory a true one? Does it really reflect the laws of the natural world?" If the experiment turned out as he predicted, then nature's answer was "Yes." But nature could also give an unexpected answer, or an utterly mystifying one. The flaw, Faraday always felt, was not nature's, but his own. Nature's laws were constant and unchanging. Either his experiment or his theory was imperfect.

Like so many other true scientists, Faraday did not set out to give man something immediately useful, but something that Faraday valued far more: understanding. In the end, he gave both. Our use of electricity followed naturally on his understanding. It was an understanding achieved, as we shall see, by the mind of a philosopher and with the hands of an experimenter.

 strange new force

We use electricity today for thousands of purposes. We use it to give us light, and to give us heat. We use it to cook, and to start a car. Countless inventions, gadgets, even toys, run on electricity.

On a broader scale, we use electricity to carry the energy of burning coal or falling water hundreds of miles, through power lines, to where it is needed. Electricity is the basis of our network of communications systems: telegraph, telephone, undersea cables. It enables us to talk to someone in the next town, or on the other side of the world. Electricity is the key force in all modern electronics devices, in radio, radar, and television.

Like Aladdin's genie, electricity seems to be devoted to answering our every need and wish. Small wonder, then, that we often take it for granted, as though it had existed, solely and always, for man's benefit and comfort. If we think about electricity at all, we probably think how much easier it makes our everyday life, or how strange and primitive our world would seem without it.

Yet go back only three hundred years, to the seventeenth century.

Most people then had never heard of electricity. To the few that had, electricity was just one of nature's odd quirks. They knew, as the Greeks had known twenty-five centuries before, that when you rubbed a piece of amber with cloth, the amber would then attract and pick up tiny objects, bits of straw and paper. Electricity *was* this feeble attracting power, nothing more, nothing less. The word electricity, in fact, comes from the Greek word for amber.

For a very few, however, this "odd quirk" would become more and more a matter of extreme interest. In laboratories in England and Europe and America, certain scientists would begin experimenting with electricity. The results would be astonishing. Each of their experiments, it seemed, would reveal something new about electricity and the way it behaved. It would keep appearing in new places, in new forms, acting in new ways. It would seem able to exist anywhere and nowhere, and follow its own strange laws.

If nothing else, these first baffling observations would convince scientists of one thing: electricity played a far bigger role in the world than the Greeks, with their amber and cloth, had ever dreamed.

Suppose you read in tomorrow's paper that a scientist had made an apple fall *up* from a tree, and rise until it disappeared into the blue. The cause, this scientist said, was a new force: antigravity. The world had always contained this force, the scientist said. We had just never happened to notice it.

All this is pure fantasy of course. But it may give us some idea of how

9

England's William Gilbert, about 1600, put forth idea that Earth itself was a magnetic body.

the concept of electricity broke upon the world. Electricity added an utterly new dimension to men's thinking. It was like discovering, not the laws of motion, but motion itself.

For a long time, many men refused to believe that there was anything new about electricity at all. They tried to fit it into what they already knew. Some thought it was a sort of inferior magnetism, weaker and less predictable than true magnetism. Some ignored it completely. In much the same way, we would probably try to explain an upward-falling apple by anything but anti-gravity. We would suspect wind currents or weather disturbance, optical illusions or even, now, electricity.

Gradually, however, the evidence on electricity built up. Often against their will, scientists concluded that they were dealing with a force never before known.

The first electrical scientist was undoubtedly William Gilbert, court physician of both Elizabeth I and James I of England. It was he who discovered that the earth itself is a giant magnet, with a north and a south pole.

Through his interest in magnetism, Gilbert was drawn to the study of electricity. He made the first methodical experiments on the attracting powers of magnetism and electricity. In doing so, Gilbert swept away much of the accumulated nonsense about the believed magical powers of "magneticks" and "electricks," as magnetized and electrified bodies were then called. Gilbert demonstrated that many substances, not just amber, could be electrified by rubbing. Among them were glass, sulphur, wax, crystals, diamonds, and a dozen other gems.

Gilbert was the first to distinguish between the attraction of magnetism and the attraction of electricity, and to compare the two forces by

10

careful experiment. His experiments were the beginning of a long trail of inquiry into the relations between electricity and magnetism that would lead, two hundred years later, to Faraday's greatest discoveries.

Gilbert's observations made possible the invention of the first "electrical machine" in 1660. The inventor was Otto von Guericke, the same German scientist who so startlingly demonstrated atmospheric pressure with his vacuumized "Magdeburg hemispheres."

Guericke took sulphur, one of Gilbert's "electricks," and out of it fashioned a solid globe about the size of a large grapefruit. He pushed an iron shaft through the sulphur globe, then mounted globe and shaft on a wooden frame. When he rotated the globe, Guericke pressed a cloth,

With a sulphur globe and an iron shaft, Otto von Guericke built first "electrical machine."

or simply his dry hand, against it. This electrified the sulphur, and it would attract paper, feathers, lint, and other small, light objects.

Guericke also noticed something else. "If you take the globe with you into a darkened room," he wrote, "and rub it, especially at night, light will result. There is likewise a virtue of sound in this globe, for when it is carried in the hand or is held in a warm hand and thus brought to the ear, roarings and crashings are heard in it."

For the first time, Guericke connected light and sound with electricity. Before, electricity had only been known as a gentle attracting force.

Guericke made still other discoveries with his sulphur globe. He observed that electricity repels objects as well as attracts them. He first saw what we now call *electrostatic induction*. An unelectrified body could be electrified (or "changed") by merely being brought near his electrified sulphur globe. Contact wasn't necessary.

Around the middle of the eighteenth century, Benjamin Franklin developed a set of terms and concepts to explain the electricity of Gilbert, Guericke, and other investigators. They proved immensely valuable and are still used today.

Let's look first at the modern explanation.

Every atom, we now say, contains protons in its nucleus and electrons outside the nucleus. Each kind of particle has a different electric charge: the proton plus ($+$) or positive and the electron minus ($-$) or negative. In its normal state, an atom contains just as many protons as electrons. It is electrically "neutral." Certain atoms, however, are able to hold more than their normal quota of electrons.

When Gilbert rubbed one of his "electricks," say, a glass rod, with a silk cloth, the force of friction shook loose a number of electrons from the glass rod. The atoms in the silk took up the free electrons. Therefore the silk had *more* electrons than usual and the glass rod had *less* electrons. So the glass rod had a positive charge, and the silk a negative charge.

The terms "plus" and "minus," "positive" and "negative," are Franklin's. He also saw that a plus and minus charge were exactly equal in strength, and could balance each other out, or neutralize each other.

We explain attraction and repulsion by saying that "like charges repel each other; unlike charges attract each other." Up to the time of Franklin, 12 it was thought that attraction and repulsion were caused by two completely different kinds of electricity. But Franklin evolved a theory of a "single electric fluid." An excess of this fluid on one body or another, he said, accounted for attraction and repulsion. This is roughly similar in

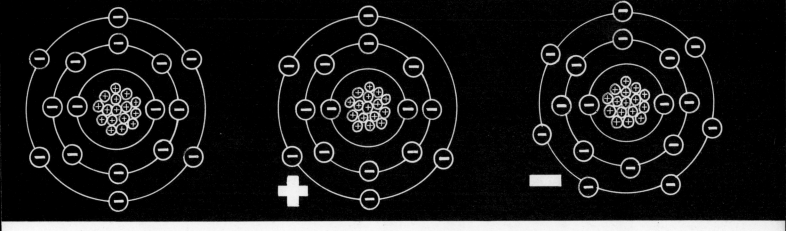

Electric charge is a matter of more or less electrons. Electrically neutral atom (left) has equal number of electrons (minus circles) and protons (plus circles). Positively charged atom (center) has one *less* electron; negatively charged atom (right) has one *more* electron than proton.

principle to our conception of electrons moving back and forth between charged bodies.

In his famous kite experiment, Franklin proved that lightning was identical to electricity produced by friction (frictional electricity). Lightning and thunder, he said, were Guericke's sparks, "roarings and crashings" tremendously enlarged.

Franklin showed electrical nature of lightning.

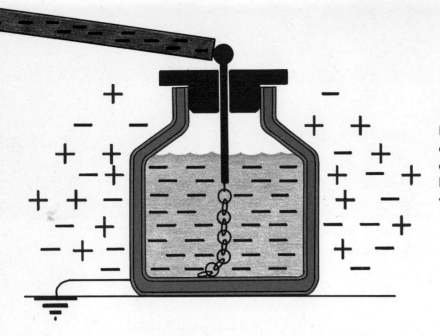

Invention of Leyden Jar, around 1700, enabled scientists momentarily to "trap" and use electricity. Charge on rod (top left) pushes its way into insulated jar, but will surge out when rod is removed.

The age of Franklin saw several refinements in producing and handling electricity. One of these was the Leyden jar, a forerunner of the device called a condenser now used in radio, telephone, and TV circuits. The Leyden jar provided a way of storing up charges like those that crackled off Guericke's globe.

A discharge from a Leyden jar could be quite impressive, as a French scientist of the time demonstrated. At a monastery in Paris, he lined up seven hundred monks, joined hand in hand. When the jar's charge was transmitted through them, all seven hundred jumped into the air.

By the time of Franklin's death, scientists had learned much about the electricity of Gilbert and Guericke. But as we now know, it was *static* electricity they were working with. This is the electricity we get when we

shuffle our feet on a wool rug, or run a hard rubber comb through our hair in dry weather.

Static electricity, as Gilbert and Guericke showed, is produced by friction between two materials and it tends to remain on one or both of those materials. This is its big drawback. It wants to stay where it has been put. Static electricity doesn't move easily, and when it does move, it jumps in a rush.

For this reason, electricity remained really nothing more than a scientist's toy in the time of Franklin. There was really nothing scientists could do with it, except observe it and play with it. There was no such thing as the electric current we use today. Guericke's machine, for example, generated static electricity: it was an electro*static* generator. Even the discharge from a Leyden jar was brief and undependable. Constant-flow electricity just didn't exist.

15

Frogs' legs twitched mysteriously when touched by
two metals. "Animal electricity," said Galvani.

Then the science of electricity took a dramatic new turn. It happened,
strangely enough, as an Italian biologist was dissecting a frog.

Luigi Galvani (1737–98) was astonished to see a frog's leg twitch
violently when he touched it simultaneously with two instruments made
of different metals. Galvani correctly supposed that the cause was electricity. But he believed the frog, by itself, produced the electricity, and
launched into a long study of "animal electricity." He was off on the
wrong trail.

It was another Italian, Alessandro Volta (1745–1827), who shaped
Galvani's discovery into one of the two most important developments in
the history of electricity. The other great development, as we shall see,
was the work of Faraday.

As he investigated "animal electricity," Volta began to doubt that
animal tissue, as such, was the source of the electricity. Instead, Volta
suspected that the electricity came from an outside source: the contact of
dissimilar metals, brass and iron, or zinc and copper, for example. He then
proceeded to create "animal electricity" without using animal tissue at all.

In 1800 Volta built the first electric battery. It was a series of zinc
and copper disks, separated by pieces of leather that had been soaked in
a weak acid solution. When he connected the zinc and copper by a wire,
electricity flowed—and *continued* to flow—around the wire. Electric current
had arrived.

16   The voltaic battery transformed electricity from a laboratory curiosity
into an invaluable scientific tool. The use of an electric current would
make possible a whole array of new experiments with a new kind of
apparatus. It would reveal new and unexpected facts about the behavior

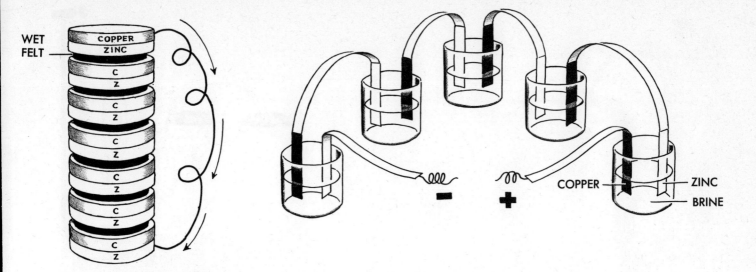

WET FELT

COPPER
ZINC

C
Z

C
Z

C
Z

C
Z

C
Z

C
Z

COPPER

ZINC

BRINE

Volta saw "animal electricity" was caused by contact of different metals and wet, often acid substance. "Volta's pile" (left) was first true electric battery. But as its felt dried, its current weakened. Volta's answer was "crown of cups" (right) in which brine could be easily replenished.

of electricity and electricity's relationship to other forces. It would enable Faraday to make his great discoveries.

For all this, the voltaic battery did have certain shortcomings. Unless there were a great many zinc and copper units ("cells"), its current was decidedly feeble. Also, as the current flowed, the zinc gradually disappeared, apparently "eaten" by the acid solution. Thus the zinc had to be continually replaced. Furthermore, nobody was exactly sure *why* the battery worked in the first place. It was Faraday, in 1834, who finally explained it.

The important thing at the time, however, was that the voltaic battery *did* work, and did generate electric current.

One of the first men to see the significance of Volta's current, and put it to brilliant use in his experiments, was a rising young English scientist, Sir Humphry Davy.

Using a many-celled voltaic battery, Davy created the first electrically produced light, completely illuminating a large lecture hall. This he did by forcing current into two carbon blocks until they heated to a blinding brilliance.

Turning the current to chemical purposes, Davy discovered two new chemical elements, potassium and sodium.

Davy made one other discovery in the early years of the nineteenth century. It would, in time, outshine his greatest laboratory triumphs.

That discovery was Faraday.

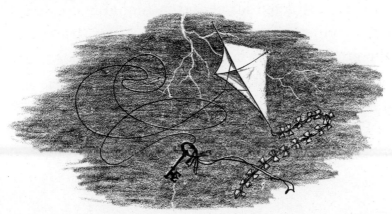

Nothing so good as an experiment

In the early 1800s England was on the eve of the Industrial Revolution. Its political leaders were beginning to grasp the great contribution science could make toward increasing England's wealth and power. Great practical inventions, improved industrial processes, often originated, they saw, in the minds of scientists. For the first time, science began to attract the attention of the general public.

In this atmosphere, two centers of scientific activity evolved in London. One was the Royal Society; the other, the Royal Institution. The Royal Institution was mainly concerned with organized experimental research. The older Royal Society was a more honorary and political body, concerned with the general advancement and application of all scientific work.

Each would play an important role in the life of Faraday.

At the Royal Institution, one spring day in 1812, Sir Humphry Davy was giving a lecture on "Metals." Still young, but with brilliant scientific discoveries behind him, Davy was England's most popular and famous scientist. He attracted large and fashionable crowds whenever he lectured. In the audience this day was Faraday, frantically trying to write down the great Davy's every word, and at the same time watch the demonstrations Davy was making.

Faraday was twenty years old at the time and (so his family thought) at the outset of a respectable career as a bookbinder and bookseller. For

FOUR LECTURES
being part of a Course on
The Elements of
CHEMICAL PHILOSOPHY
Delivered by
SIR H. DAVY
LL.D. Sec Rs. FRSE. MRIA. MRI. &c. &c.
AT THE
Royal Institution
And taken off from Notes
BY
M FARADAY
1812

the past seven years he had been learning his trade, and now his apprenticeship was nearly over. There was only one trouble: Faraday had no desire to become a bookbinder.

From an extremely poor family, Faraday had had only the rudiments of a school education. School time had often been used to earn a few pennies running errands for London shopkeepers. However, when he was apprenticed to a bookbinder, Faraday's fortunes improved. He began to read the books in the shop, and his interests soon leveled on "philosophy"—the scientific kind. His employer was a generous and sympathetic man, and encouraged Faraday in his studies. By the time he was nineteen, Faraday had consumed most of the basic science books then existing in English, and had built both his own voltaic battery and his own electrostatic generator. With these he repeated many of the experiments he had read about.

19

In the spring of 1810, Faraday went to hear a series of chemistry lectures. He took neat, detailed notes, added diagrams and illustrations, and bound the material into a four-volume set. Eventually one of the bookbinder's scientific customers happened to see these books. Highly impressed with Faraday's obvious scientific talent, he bought Faraday tickets to four of Davy's lectures at the Royal Institution.

These lectures convinced Faraday, once and for all, that he was going to be a "philosopher." Again, at Davy's lectures, he took copious notes, and again he bound and illustrated them. This time, though, he sent the books directly to Davy, with a request for work in the laboratory of the Royal Institution. Davy, though impressed, refused to hire Faraday. He already had a regular lab assistant. Besides, Davy asked, why should Faraday want to give up his respectable and secure future for science? Science, Davy said, was a field that offered little security, salary, or opportunity for advancement. A few months later, however, Davy's regular lab assistant departed, and Faraday was hired.

"The explosion was so rapid as to blow my hand open."

If Faraday had thought science would be exciting, he soon found he was right, all too right. One of his first jobs was to assist Davy in an attempt to obtain pure nitrogen from one of its compounds, nitrogen trichloride. The attempt failed; but not, as he wrote a friend, for lack of effort:

"I have escaped (not quite unhurt) from four different and strong explosions of the substance [nitrogen trichloride]. Of these the most terrible was when I was holding between my thumb and finger a small tube containing 7½ grains of it. My face was within twelve inches of the tube; but I fortunately had on a glass mask. The explosion was so rapid as to blow my hand open, tear off a part of one nail, and has made my fingers so sore that I cannot yet use them easily. The pieces of the tube were projected with such force as to cut the glass face of the mask I had on. On repeating the experiment this morning the tube and a receiver were blown to pieces. I got a cut on my eyelid, and Sir H. bruised his hand. The experiment was repeated again with a larger portion of the substance. It stood for a moment or two, and then exploded with a fearful noise: both Sir H. and I had masks on, but I escaped this time the best. Sir H. had his face cut in two places about the chin, and a violent blow on the forehead struck through a considerable thickness of silk and leather; and with this experiment he has for the present concluded."

21

Not many months after their violent encounter with nitrogen trichloride, Davy set off on a tour of the universities and laboratories of Europe, and Faraday went with him.

The trip was not altogether a pleasant one for Faraday for two reasons. One was the haughty Lady Davy, the other was the fact that he was often obliged to act as Davy's valet. But the trip's benefits were great. Faraday met and talked with the great European scientists of the age, among them Volta, Ampère, Gay-Lussac, and Von Humboldt. In eighteen months, the tour gave him a broadness and depth of scientific knowledge that might otherwise have taken years of independent study to acquire.

Back in England, Faraday continued to work in Davy's shadow. Davy's research tended to move in quick bursts of energy and insight, and Faraday was invaluable in giving it some order and method. Davy's invention of the miner's safety lamp, introduced in English coal mines in 1816, owed much to Faraday.

Gradually, Faraday moved out on his own. His name began to appear more and more frequently in the scientific journals of the day.

One of his articles concerned a new metal, "sirium," that an Austrian chemist claimed to have discovered. Faraday reported that he had carefully analyzed a sample of sirium. Step by step, he had broken it down into iron, sulphur, cobalt, nickel, a trace or two of other metals, and that left . . . nothing. Sirium was nothing but a compound of metals already known.

He made two important chemical discoveries. The first was a method of making liquid chlorine, an element which is naturally a gas in its pure, isolated form. This enabled Davy and other scientists to liquefy several other gaseous elements.

The second discovery was benzene, a compound of hydrogen and carbon, which is of basic importance in the understanding of organic

22

Hired to accompany the famous Davy on a tour of the science centers of Europe, Faraday soon found that Sir Humphry and Lady Davy had rather curious ideas about the duties of a "scientific assistant."

chemistry. Benzene is also a key chemical in dyemaking, perfume making, and in certain pharmaceutical products.

The Royal Society could no longer do without the name Faraday, and in 1824 he was elected to membership. The following year, Davy resigned as director of the Royal Institution laboratory, and Faraday was appointed as his successor. Faraday had now reached the pinnacle of his worldly ambition: he was an acknowledged "philosopher."

Faraday's marvelous talents as an experimenter were becoming clear to English scientists. He himself had the highest faith in the value of experimenting. "*Criticise* one's own view in every way by experiment,"

23

For six long years, at the request of the Royal Society, Faraday devoted much time and energy to perfecting lens glass for microscopes and telescopes. Then, in 1830, he asked to be relieved of the task.

he once jotted in his notebook; "if possible leave no objection to be put by others." Later in life, he wrote: "I have far more confidence in the one man who works mentally and bodily at a matter than in the six who merely talk about it. *Nothing is so good as an experiment* which, whilst it sets error right, gives an absolute advancement in knowledge."

In 1827, Faraday wrote a classic book on the art of experimenting. It was called *Chemical Manipulation*. It was reprinted twice, and probably would have been reprinted many more times. But Faraday refused to authorize the printing of even a fourth edition. He felt the book had become outdated. Perhaps so, but it is still recommended by chemistry professors as a fine primer on research methods.

Beginning in 1825, Faraday set off on a long investigation of optical glass. This work was done at the request of the Royal Society, and its express purpose was to find how to manufacture better lenses for telescopes and microscopes.

For six years, Faraday gave much of his time and energy to the task. Progress was slow. Working with molten glass and a white-hot furnace was a tricky and exhausting business. Finally, in 1830, he produced a piece of glass which met the expectations of the Royal Society. Pleased, the Society asked Faraday to make as large and as perfect a piece of the glass as he could.

In the politest terms, Faraday refused. To the Royal Society he wrote: "I should, under circumstances of perfect freedom, assent to it at once; but obliged as I have been to devote the whole of my spare time to glass-making, and consequently to resign the pursuit of such philosophical inquiries as suggested themselves to my own mind, I would wish under the present circumstances to lay the glass aside for a while, that I may enjoy the pleasure of working out my own thoughts on other subjects. . . ."

Faraday's "own thoughts on other subjects," we can be sure, were not as vague as he made them sound. They were focused on electromagnetism, the study of the relationship between the forces of magnetism and electricity. He had already made an important discovery in this field.

About 1820, the Danish physicist Hans Oersted (1777–1851) had made a far-reaching discovery. Almost by accident, he had observed that the magnetic needle of a compass, if first lined up parallel to a wire, veers out at right angles when a voltaic current is passed through the wire. When the direction of the current is reversed, the needle swings out the other way, and remains there, at nearly right angles to the wire, as long as the current flows in that direction.

For the first time, Oersted had seen the magnetic effect of an electric current. Electricity, like the common magnet, could attract magnetic materials. This discovery spurred tremendous interest in the whole field of electromagnetism. Many scientists set to work to extend and explain Oersted's experiments.

Unquestionably, the greatest immediate practical benefit of Oersted's discovery was the invention of the electromagnet. In England in 1825, William Sturgeon had bent an ordinary bar into a horseshoe, coated it with varnish, and wrapped it round and round with bare copper wire. When he ran current from a voltaic battery through the wire, the horse-

Oersted discovered first definite link between magnetism and electricity. He lined up magnetic needle parallel to wire (1). When current was passed through wire (2), needle swung out to almost right angles. When Oersted reversed the current (3), needle swung out the other way.

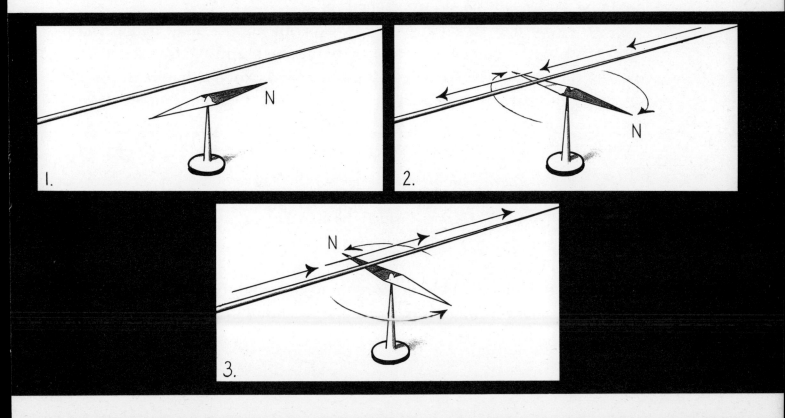

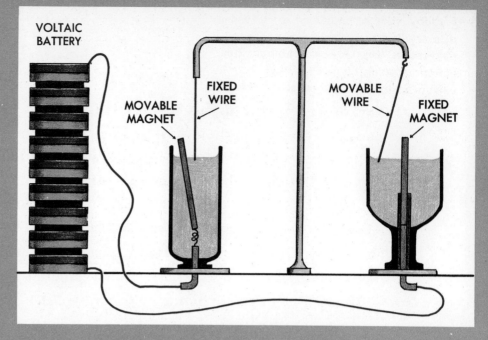

VOLTAIC
BATTERY

MOVABLE
MAGNET

FIXED
WIRE

MOVABLE
WIRE

FIXED
MAGNET

With this ingenious apparatus, Faraday proved that electric current exerted a circular magnetic force around a wire. When current from voltaic battery was turned on, movable magnet rotated about fixed wire, and movable wire about fixed magnet. This experiment won Faraday his first great fame.

shoe had become a magnet, capable of supporting a weight of nine pounds. From Sturgeon's principle, stronger and stronger electromagnets were developed.

At the Royal Institution, meanwhile, Davy himself had plunged into a study of the curious interaction between the forces of magnetism and electricity. By Davy's side, naturally, had been Faraday, and as usual he had missed nothing. Thus when a good friend, editor of a scientific journal, had asked him to write an article on the "History of Electro-Magnetism," Faraday had been ready and willing to oblige.

As he was writing this long and detailed paper, Faraday had done a characteristic thing. He had repeated all the important experiments that had ever been made on electromagnetism.

When he had repeated Oersted's experiments, Faraday had been intrigued by the magnetic needle swinging back and forth under the wire as the current was started, stopped, reversed. Nobody had really explained this curious back-and-forth movement. Oersted himself was puzzled, and had suggested vaguely that the cause was some kind of "conflict of electricity" based on a series of attractions and repulsions in the wire.

Faraday, though, had soon had more definite ideas. He had discarded the "conflict" theory. Instead, he had begun to visualize the wire exerting a continuous *circular* force at right angles to its axis. In a matter of days he had set up experiments to test that theory.

The experiments had been more than successful. Not only, Faraday discovered, could he make a movable magnet rotate completely around

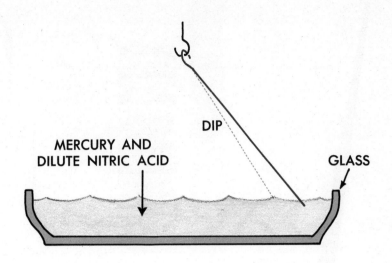

Faraday made current-carrying wire move as a result of being in Earth's magnetic field alone. "Dip" is angle of magnetism at various points on globe, would not exist at Earth's N and S magnetic poles.

DIP

MERCURY AND
DILUTE NITRIC ACID

GLASS

a fixed, current-carrying wire. He could also do the reverse: a movable current-carrying wire would rotate around a fixed magnet. He had found too—and this seemed like pure magic to some—that he could make a delicately balanced, current-carrying wire rotate by positioning it in the *earth's* magnetic field alone.

These "electromagnetic rotations" had received world-wide attention back in 1821. Yet they had brought Faraday, and other scientists, a new and vexing problem. Its solution had eluded the best investigators ever since. If an electric current could create magnetism, why, then, shouldn't the opposite be true? Why shouldn't magnetism be able to create electric current?

As early as 1822, Faraday had considered the possibility, jotting down in his notebook the simple challenge: "Convert magnetism into electricity." In the following years, he tried and failed four times.

Now, in 1831, he was on the verge of answering this momentous riddle.

Announcing: our age of electricity

As he began setting up the experiments that would bring him his greatest fame, Faraday was virtually certain that magnetism *could* be converted into electricity. True, he had failed four times. Others had also failed. It might not be he who succeeded, and it might take a hundred years. But someday, Faraday thought, someone would do it.

Although Faraday wasn't aware of it, his conviction was based on a fundamental law of nature. This law was not even stated until twenty years later, and not completely accepted for another fifty. It was the law of conservation of energy: *It is impossible to create or destroy energy—what disappears in one form must reappear in another.* Instinctively, Faraday guessed that it should be possible to convert one kind of energy into another. Each kind of energy—mechanical, chemical, magnetic, electric, heat (later he added even light and gravity)—must have a definite relationship to every other kind. Therefore, all that was necessary to show these relationships was the proper equipment and the right experiment.

In this spirit, Faraday began his fifth attempt to convert magnetism into electricity. The equipment he chose consisted of an iron ring, two coils of copper wire, a voltaic battery, and a meter for detecting small amounts of electric current (galvanometer). Around one side of the iron ring he wound the first coil of wire, ready to be connected to the voltaic battery. Around the other side, he wound his second coil of wire. This he connected to the galvanometer.

Faraday knew that when current from the battery flowed in the first wire, the iron ring would become an electromagnet. Then, he hoped, the magnetic energy would cause a current to flow in the second wire. If so, the needle of the galvanometer would register the new current by swinging one way or the other.

It worked. But in a quite unexpected way.

At the very instant he connected the battery, the needle of the galvanometer jumped, then fell back to the "no current" position. When he broke the connection the needle jumped the other way, and fell back. Between making and breaking the connection, the galvanometer registered "no current" in the second wire.

Faraday was cautious about leaping to conclusions. He asked himself: Was it really magnetism that caused the current in the second wire? Or could it be a direct reaction to the current in the first wire? To check this, he used, instead of the iron ring, a copper one. Copper would not be magnetized by the electric current. On making and breaking the connection this time, the needle of the galvanometer quivered ever so slightly, far less than when the iron ring had been used. Faraday would come back to that tiny quiver later. Now, however, he had satisfied himself that it *was* magnetism producing the current, and proceeded to work out the details of this great discovery.

First, Faraday found that an iron bar worked just as well as his iron ring. Then he found that using an electromagnet was by no means necessary. An ordinary bar magnet, wrapped round with one coil of wire, could produce currents in the wire. Going one step further, he found that the wire did not even have to be wrapped around the bar magnet. All he had to do was move a magnet close to a coil of wire, and the galvanometer needle would jump. Move it away, and the needle would jump the other way.

Rotating a copper disk between the poles of a giant horseshoe magnet, Faraday ushered in the age of electricity by generating a constant electric current from magnetism. Detailed diagram at right shows disk's axle (A) and its rim (B). Rim lies between poles of magnet (C). Wire (D) is in contact with both axle and rim. As copper disk (E) was rotated by Faraday, current showed on galvanometer (F) connected by wire to axle and rim. Later, Faraday said apparatus worked because copper disk was "cutting magnetic lines of force."

The important thing, Faraday concluded, was *motion*. The magnet and the wire had to be moving toward each other, or away from each other, to produce current. When neither was moving, no current flowed. To make continuous current, therefore, he knew he had to make the motion continuous.

Faraday solved this problem by substituting a copper disk for the copper wire. He mounted the disk between the poles of a giant horseshoe magnet, and added a crank so he could rotate the disk with his hand. Two wires ran from the disk and met in a galvanometer. One of the wires was connected to the axle of the disk, the other rode on the disk's rim. As he rotated the disk, a steady current registered on the galvanometer. When he reversed the rotation of the disk, the galvanometer also showed a steady current, but in the opposite direction. The world's first electromagnetic generator was in operation.

Current was being *induced* from magnetism. Although Faraday called this "magneto-electric induction," the modern term is "electromagnetic induction."

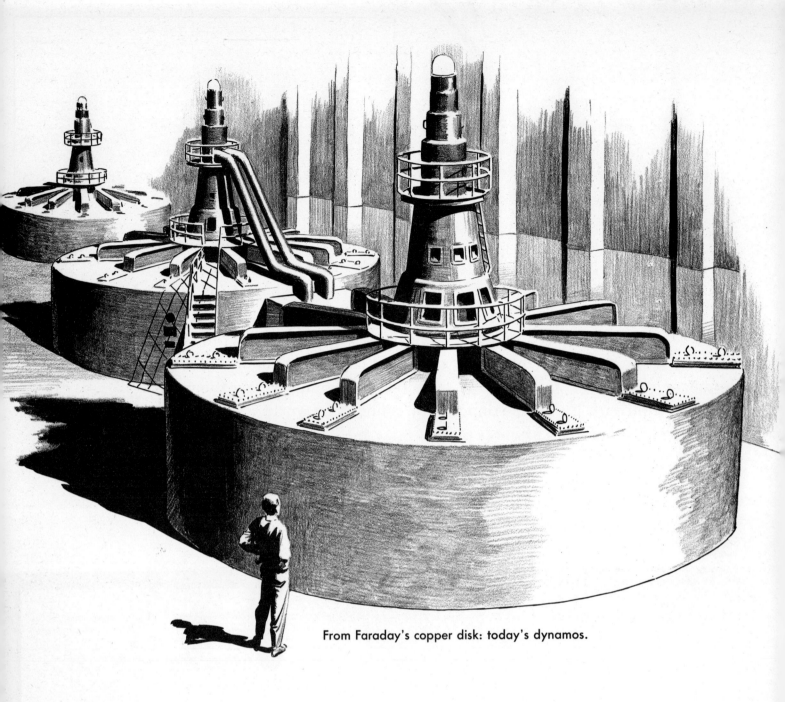

From Faraday's copper disk: today's dynamos.

The huge 100,000-horsepower dynamos of today are based directly on Faraday's electromagnetic generator, both in principle and construction. In the huge modern generators, the mechanical energy that Faraday himself supplied in rotating his copper disk is now supplied by steam or falling water. Thus the mechanical energy available is practically unlimited, and tremendous supplies of current can be generated and transmitted to wherever electrical power is needed.

In explaining the action of his electromagnetic generator, Faraday shocked his scientific colleagues by introducing, out of the blue, an entirely new concept. The generator worked, he said, because the copper disk was "cutting the magnetic lines of force." This was what converted the magnetism into electric current.

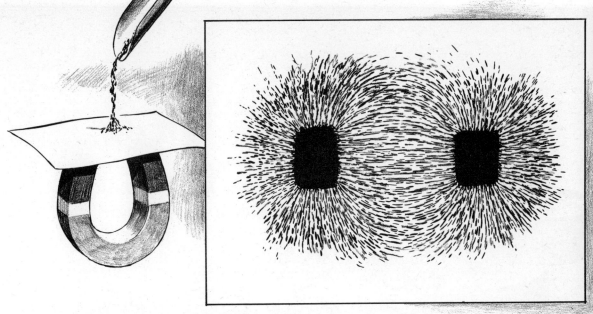

Iron filings, said Faraday, plainly revealed "magnetic lines of force."

When iron filings are sprinkled around the poles of a horseshoe magnet they arrange themselves in curved lines forming a definite pattern. The iron filings, Faraday said, revealed the magnetic lines of force, and all of them together represented the "magnetic field." Faraday considered these lines of force as real but invisible bands, linking the two poles. This theory would be scoffed at by many scientists for many years, but it would lead Faraday far out ahead of his time, into the very center of modern physics.

No sooner had Faraday demonstrated electromagnetic induction than he turned back to those tiny currents he had noticed when using a copper ring instead of an iron ring. To make sure that the currents had nothing to do with magnetism, he wrapped his two coils around an ordinary wood bobbin. Again the galvanometer registered slight currents on making and breaking the connection to the voltaic battery. There could be only one explanation: the voltaic current in the first wire was inducing a new electric current in the second wire.

Faraday called his discovery "Volta-electric induction." On it are based three highly important electrical devices: the transformer, the induction coil, and the coupled circuit. Each plays a large role in enabling us to use the electrical power generated by our modern dynamos.

Faraday had performed all his experiments on induced currents in less than three months. In November, 1831, he reported their splendid results to the Royal Society, and went off for a short rest at the seashore. It was a well-earned rest: the discoveries he had made in those three months would transform the face of the world.

For the next several months, Faraday's electrical research stopped. He was occupied with other duties and responsibilities. Both the Royal Society and the Royal Institution made heavy demands on his time. In the summer of 1832, however, he was back on electricity.

Now, Faraday in his own mind was certain that the electric current he had produced with his magnets and wires was no different from Volta's current or any other kind of electricity. But others weren't so sure. Galvani and Volta, even Davy, had believed that there were "different electricities." The discharge from a Leyden jar, for example, was thought to be different from a voltaic current. The belief still lingered in the 1830s.

Faraday wanted to clear up the matter for good. He began by making a list of all the effects any electric generator—electrostatic, voltaic, electromagnetic—had ever been known to produce. The effects were: (1) heat; (2) magnetism; (3) the electric spark; (4) the "Galvanic" effect on animal tissue; (5) the ability to break up chemical compounds when they were dissolved in water. This last effect is known as electrochemical decomposition, or simply "electrolysis." In it, for example, table salt or sodium chloride (chemical formula $NaCl$) will break up into sodium (Na) and chlorine (Cl).

Any and all of these five effects, Faraday then showed, could be produced by each kind of electric generator. The apparent "different electricities," it appeared, were only differences in strength and quantity of electricity in motion.

To remove the last shred of doubt, Faraday surveyed all the examples of electricity: (1) static or frictional; (2) voltaic; (3) electromagnetic; (4) animal; (5) thermal (electricity produced by the effect of different temperatures in different parts of the same body). Then, setting up a series of eight tests, Faraday recorded how examples of each type of electricity reacted to each of the eight tests. The reactions were remarkably similar for all five types.

At last, Faraday could announce: "Electricity, whatever may be its source, is identical in nature." He was very sure, now, that no one would give him an argument.

Already Faraday had made gigantic forward strides toward the understanding and use of electricity. He had cleared up much half-truth, or "doubtful knowledge" as he called it. He had explained seemingly unexplainable facts, and he had discovered new ways of generating electricity. Perhaps another man would have rested on his laurels. But Faraday felt he still had some unfinished business. That business concerned

34

NaCl   Na   Cl

In water, a molecule of table salt (left) parts into its two elements: sodium (top right) and chlorine (bottom right). This easing-apart in water is typical of salts and many other types of chemical compounds.

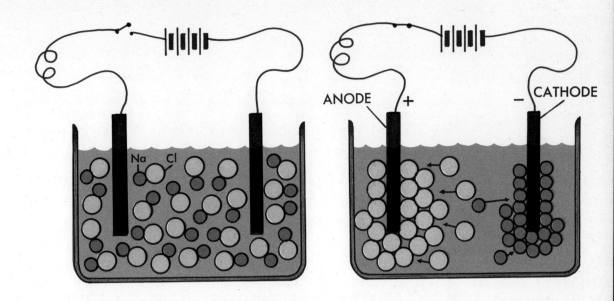

In electrolysis, electric current finishes the splitting-up that water has begun. Chlorine (Cl) is drawn to the anode pole, where it bubbles to the surface; sodium (Na) is drawn to the cathode.

electrochemistry, and it would occupy him for the next several years.

When he had been proving the identity of all electricity, Faraday had become intrigued by an electric current's ability to decompose chemical compounds. Thirty years before, Davy had used this power to discover sodium and potassium.

Davy had used what we now call an "electrolytic cell." This consists of an enclosed glass trough, through the top of which are inserted two metal poles, connected by wires to a voltaic battery. In the trough can be placed one of many kinds of chemical *solutions,* chemical compounds dissolved in water. When the current is turned on, the compound seems to break apart. If the compound were common salt, sodium would begin to appear at one of the poles, and chlorine at the other.

Davy and others explained this by saying that when the current was turned on, the two poles became charged. The resulting stress then simply tore the compound apart.

Faraday couldn't accept this explanation. In the first place, he knew that chemical attraction was tremendously powerful. (This is the force which binds atoms of two elements together in a molecule.) Yet, strangely, the atoms could be separated by the most feeble voltaic current.

Furthermore, he found, the size of the metal poles, and their distance apart, made absolutely no difference. The poles could be the size of clothes pins, or the size of baseball bats, and still would decompose the same weight of chemicals. And the poles could be six inches or six feet apart. Yet if the poles themselves actually *did* tear apart compounds, Faraday reasoned, their size and distance apart should have a very definite effect on the final results. What was the real explanation?

The key factor, Faraday discovered, was the quantity of electricity used. More electricity would decompose a greater weight of chemicals;

35

less current, less weight. This discovery became known as Faraday's "First law of electrolysis." It led Faraday to devise the voltameter: the first, and for many years the only, accurate instrument for measuring quantities of electricity.

But *how* did the current break up the compound molecules? Here was a problem that experiment couldn't solve. It was obviously impossible to watch electricity acting on a molecule. And the action's visible effects—chemicals deposited at the poles—weren't any help either. Using what knowledge he did have, and putting his high imaginative power to work, Faraday formed a theory, one that agrees in every important way with our modern theory.

Faraday claimed that an electric current passing through a solution, instead of violently ripping molecules apart, gently eased one of the atoms away from the other. Take a molecule of salt. If dry, the sodium atom and the chlorine atom cling tightly to each other because of chemical attraction. If, however, salt is dissolved in water, the atoms cling less tightly: the sodium atom is also attracted by the chlorine atoms of neighboring salt molecules, as well as by its own chlorine atom. Thus forces are already at work to separate the molecule. The electric current merely encourages and guides the separation, and the separated atoms, now called "ions," drift with the current toward the two metal poles.

To wipe out all traces of the old theory of electrochemical decomposition, Faraday invented a completely new set of terms. He felt "poles" still suggested that the molecules were torn apart. He renamed them "electrodes" (derived from Greek, suggesting "current paths"). "The poles," he explained, "are merely the surfaces or doors by which the electricity enters into, or passes out of, the substance suffering decomposition." It was he who termed the chemical solution, the "electrolyte." "Ion," too, is his term, as is "electrolysis." These terms are part of the scientific vocabulary of every modern scientist.

Scientists are not the only ones who have profited from Faraday's work on electrolysis. His discoveries and laws underlie the whole modern process of electroplating. Gold-plated jewelry, silver-plated forks and spoons, chromium-plated car bumpers, are just a few of the products of electroplating. Another practical benefit has been the bulk production of aluminum and several other metals. These are extracted from the natural ores by electrolysis. Finally, the modern method of printing known as "electrotype" is based on the principles discovered by Faraday.

With the understanding he had gained of electrolysis, Faraday next turned to an old puzzle: the cause of the current from a voltaic battery. Volta found that when he merely touched the copper plate to the zinc plate, without any acid solution between them, one plate became positively charged and the other negatively charged. However, no current flowed until the acid solution was added. Much as he had with the electrolytic cell, Volta assumed that the plates somehow pulled current from the acid solution.

Faraday soon offered the new, and correct, explanation. He saw that the acid solution was equivalent to the electrolyte in the electrolytic cell, and the plates equivalent to the electrodes. There was only one difference. In electrolysis, the ions were taken from the electrolyte and deposited on the electrodes. In the voltaic battery, the ions were taken from the zinc plate and then combined with the acid solution. This is what produced the current. Thus, as a battery runs, the zinc plate slowly disappears, "eaten" by the acid. As electrolysis takes place, it is the salt that slowly disappears from the electrolyte, appearing on the electrodes as sodium and chlorine.

As Faraday reached the end of his research in electrochemistry, he was satisfied that he had given scientists a clearer, truer picture of the voltaic battery and electrolysis. But for him, the experiments also had a deeper meaning: they showed a definite relationship between chemical energy and electrical energy.

Here's why. In electrolysis, the energy of the electric current helps to overpower the energy of chemical attraction. That's one relationship. In the voltaic battery, the energy of chemical attraction is changed into the energy of an electric current. Specifically, the chemical reaction of zinc

Close relationship between electrolysis and voltaic battery was proved by Faraday. In electrolysis, current is used up in breaking apart chemicals, sodium and chlorine. In voltaic battery, current is made by combining chemicals, zinc and acid. So voltaic battery is electrolysis, but backwards.

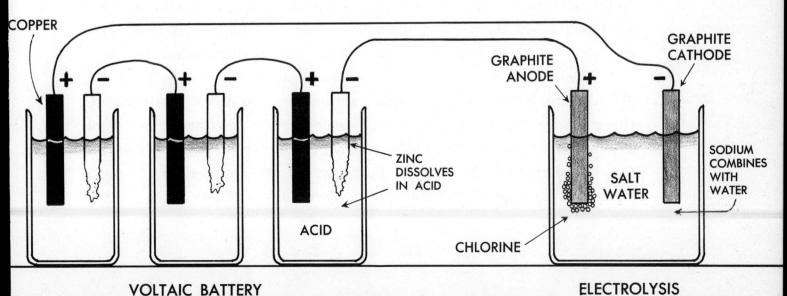

COPPER

ZINC DISSOLVES IN ACID

ACID

GRAPHITE ANODE

GRAPHITE CATHODE

SALT WATER

SODIUM COMBINES WITH WATER

CHLORINE

VOLTAIC BATTERY

ELECTROLYSIS

and acid produces the current. Ions combining into a molecule make a current, and a current separates a molecule back into ions. In other words, as Faraday put it, "chemical action is electricity, and electricity is chemical action."

A great period in Faraday's career was now drawing to a close. The year was 1839. Beginning with the discovery of electromagnetic induction in the fall of 1831, he had ranged far and wide through the whole field of electricity. What he had found as a disorganized mass of half-truths and unexplained facts, he had turned into an orderly and useful body of knowledge. His future work would be less a matter of correcting and explaining, and more a matter of seeking new facts, relationships, and laws.

During these eight years, he had made some five thousand individual experiments, each of which he meticulously described and explained in his notebooks. These became the first section of his great lifework, *Experimental Researches in Electricity,* published in 1855. The three big volumes of this work are still a treasure-house of information for physicists and electrical engineers.

The amount of sheer physical and mental effort that Faraday had put into this research awed his fellow scientists. A well-known French scientist of the time, Auguste de la Rive, wrote about him: "Every morning Faraday went into his laboratory as the man of business goes to his office, and then tried by experiment the truth of the ideas which he had conceived overnight, as ready to give them up if experiment said *no* as to follow them out with rigorous logic if experiment said *yes.*"

Faraday would soon have to ease up on the tremendous pace he had set for himself during these eight years. It had taken a heavy toll on his physical and mental stamina. However, near the very end of this period, Farady began a study that would have a deep influence on much of his later work.

Guericke and others, we know, had shown that a charged body could electrify an uncharged body without touching it, in what is called electrostatic induction. Faraday wondered why this happened. How could electricity exert such an effect through air and other substances?

The accepted theory did not satisfy Faraday a bit. It held that electrostatic induction was simply "action at a distance." Little, if anything, happened in the intervening space between a charged body and an uncharged body. The only important thing, according to this theory, was the charged body itself. To Faraday, this all sounded like so much nonsense. He just couldn't conceive of such "action at a distance." It was

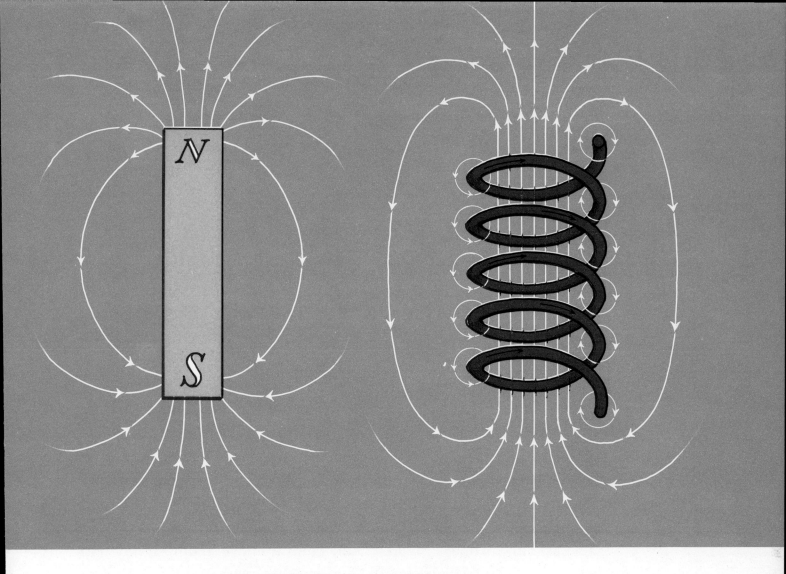

Faraday showed that a bar magnet (left) and a coil
of current-carrying wire (right) have a similar
"electromagnetic field." Thus a soft iron core inserted in the coil would make an electromagnet.

like thinking a flick of your finger could knock down a distant building.

Faraday went back to the lines of force he had first visualized in explaining his electromagnetic generator. Around a magnet, he had said, these lines were always present. They were real but invisible. Together, they made up a magnetic field, which could be roughly represented by iron filings.

Like magnetism, Faraday concluded, electricity also produced lines of force and therefore what he called an "electric field." In electrostatic induction, these lines of force stretched across, through the intervening substance, and touched the other body. Thus the two bodies were really in contact with each other. It was no longer necessary for him to think of "action at a distance."

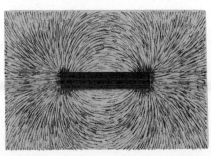
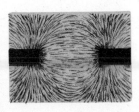

The way of a philosopher

By the early 1840s, Faraday had inherited Sir Humphry Davy's position as England's foremost man of science. As Davy had, Faraday now drew large and fashionable crowds to his lectures at the Royal Institution.

Perhaps the most famous of these lectures were the ones at Christmas for children, which Faraday delivered for nineteen seasons. One of them, "The Chemical History of a Candle," can even now be found in book form in most libraries, and still makes lively and informative reading.

Faraday's Christmas lecture on "Metals" so impressed one fourteen-year-old boy that he wrote a personal thank-you note to Faraday, adding, "I can assure you that I shall always cherish with great pleasure the recollection of having been assisted in my early studies in Chemistry by so distinguished a man." The boy's name: Albert Edward, Prince of Wales, the future Edward VII of England.

Faraday's other public lectures were to adult audiences, describing the latest advances (many of them his own) in scientific experiment and theory. When giving these lectures, Faraday always tried to make sure that even the most unscientific of his listeners would be able to understand them. The lectures were never just fact, figure, and theory, but were filled with demonstrations and examples. Besides, they were fun, as one description of the time indicates: "Faraday explained the magnet and strength of attraction. He made us all laugh heartily; and when he threw a coal-scuttle full of coals, a poker, and a pair of tongs at the great magnet,

and they stuck there, the theater echoed with shouts of laughter."

Although they seemed effortless, Faraday put a great many hours of work into preparing his lectures, and he continued to do so throughout his most exhausting periods of original research. Even, as later, when his health often broke down, the Royal Institution lectures were the last duty he would give up, and the first he would resume on his recovery.

Faraday gave so much time and effort to his lectures for a special reason of his own. He felt he owed the Royal Institution a great debt of gratitude for starting him on his life as a "philosopher." The lectures were his way of repaying that debt. In these years, the Royal Institution was constantly in need of money for its research projects, and Faraday's brilliant lectures did much to bring it the public attention and support it needed. The mere presence of Faraday was invaluable to the Royal Institution. If he abandoned it, Faraday realized, it faced failure.

This loyalty never diminished. As his fame grew, Faraday was offered many better-paying and less strenuous positions than his one as director of the Royal Institution laboratory. All of them he turned down.

41

In one letter of refusal, he wrote: "I think it a matter of duty and gratitude on my part to do what I can for the Royal Institution in the present attempt to establish it firmly. The Institution has been a source of knowledge and pleasure to me. . . . I remember the protection it has afforded me during the past years of my scientific life. . . ."

Faraday had another lifelong loyalty, this one broader and more complex than his loyalty to the Royal Institution. It was to "philosophy," and for Faraday its first requirement was complete independence of mind. He felt a philosopher should give his whole mind—never just part of it—in the search of truth.

It was on these grounds that he declined, at different times, both the presidency of the Royal Institution and the presidency of the Royal Society. The presidents of these two bodies, Faraday knew, were forced to take sides in the scientific controversies of the day, often before fully understanding the questions involved. That thought didn't appeal at all to Faraday. To John Tyndall, the man who would eventually succeed him as director of the Royal Institution, Faraday remarked, "Tyndall, I must remain plain Michael Faraday to the last, and let me now tell you, that if I accepted the presidency of the Royal Society, I could not answer for the integrity of my intellect for a single year."

Knighthood was also offered to Faraday, and he declined it. *Sir Michael Faraday*, he believed, would have a built-in social significance that Michael Faraday, the philosopher, didn't need or want.

Faraday considered wealth just as superfluous for a philosopher as social prestige. Starting in the 1820s, up until his discovery of electromagnetic induction, he had done some work as a scientific consultant for several industrial firms. This "professional business," as he called it, became more and more profitable every year. If he had kept it up, he would have died a wealthy man. Instead, Faraday decided that it was taking entirely too much time and thought away from his experimental research, and dropped it almost completely. He died with little money.

To us this seems like a tremendous sacrifice for science. But Faraday looked at it differently. It was a simple choice between the pursuit of wealth and the pursuit of natural truth. Calmly, and without any thoughts of self-sacrifice, he chose the pursuit of natural truth.

42   For much the same reason, Faraday spent little time thinking about practical applications for his own discoveries. If he had lived to see them, he would have been delighted by the electrical inventions of Edison and Bell and Morse. He would probably roam happily through a modern

Under Faraday's guidance, first electromagnetic
generator lighted beacon of an English lighthouse.

house, flipping electrical switches and turning electrical knobs. But he
himself rarely considered how his electrical discoveries could be put to
use. Practical applications would come in time, he felt, and meanwhile,
he had more pressing work.

Often, when asked what *use* a certain discovery had, Faraday liked to
quote Benjamin Franklin's answer to the same question. "What use is
it?" Franklin shot back. "What is the use of a baby? Someday it will
grow up."

However, there was one bit of "professional business" that Faraday
couldn't resist. He became scientific adviser on the illumination of Eng-
lish lighthouses. About 1860, at Dungeness lighthouse on the English
Channel, he supervised the installation of an electromagnetic generator.
Its purpose: to provide current for the lighthouse's carbon-arc beacon.
This was the first practical application of his great discovery.

In 1841, from sheer mental and physical exhaustion,
Faraday broke down. But when he finally resumed
his research in 1845, his experiments were more
intricate and his theories bolder than ever before.

Throughout the 1830s, as we have seen, Faraday had worked his mind and body to the limits of their endurance. In 1841, overwork finally caught up with him. He suffered a severe physical breakdown, and was forced to give up all experimental research for the next four years. Although Faraday recovered and went on, in the next fifteen years, to do trail-blazing scientific work, his breakdown had some serious after-effects. The most serious was an increasing loss of memory. This finally caused him, a full five years before he died in 1867, to give up his research altogether.

Just before he made that painful decision in March of 1862, Faraday had caught himself repeating the same experiments he had made just a day or two before.

It was too much. Faraday's loyalty to his philosophy was too great to tolerate such a lapse in his mental powers, and he never made another experiment.

44

But in one way, Faraday's breakdown was beneficial. Forced to rest, his mind wandered back over the experiments and discoveries of twenty years. He began to see, in full perspective, not only what his experiments had proved about electricity, but what they unmistakably suggested about the entire natural world and the forces that shape it.

First, Faraday saw that all his major discoveries had really been variations on one great theme: the relationship of different forces. Magnetic force became electrical. Electrical attraction became chemical attraction. All forms of electricity were identical. Faraday had always instinctively believed in the conservation of energy. Now that belief took a deeper turn. There was, he came to believe, a harmony between *all* the forces of nature, including light and gravity. Perhaps, he ventured, they were merely the different disguises of one all-inclusive force, governed by one all-inclusive law.

Second, Faraday became convinced that his magnetic and electrical "lines of force" were not purely imaginary, but were as real and important as the substances from which they came. He began to suspect, too, that these lines of force might not only apply to magnetism and electricity. Other kinds of invisible energy—heat, light, even gravity—might also be connected with them.

On these two basic ideas, Faraday built the remarkable theories of his last active years. Very few of the theories would turn out to be wrong. Some, Faraday himself would prove by experiment. Others, he would lack the means to prove, and their prophetic truth would only become clear to future generations of scientists.

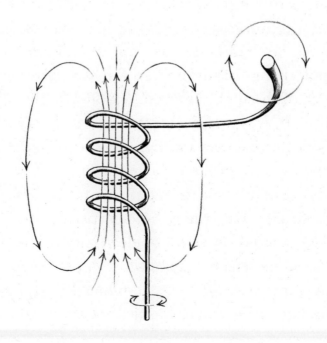

ost singular speculations

Light energy, Faraday believed, was no different from any other kind of energy. If so, it should show a definite link with those other kinds. After he resumed his research in 1845, Faraday wasted little time before demonstrating such a link.

He showed the effect of magnetic force on light. Ordinary light, as it travels, vibrates in all directions. But if it is passed through special prisms, light can be made to vibrate in only one direction. This is polarized light. Magnetism, Faraday observed, twisted the direction, or *plane,* of the vibrations in a ray of polarized light.

In one way, this discovery was a reward for that long and arduous research Faraday had once done on optical glass. At first, using many different polarizing prisms, he had failed to observe anything. Then he tried a block of the highly pure and uniform glass he had made twenty years before. It was when this block was placed across the poles of a powerful electromagnet, and light passed through it, that Faraday first observed the twisting of the polarized ray.

Faraday couldn't believe that magnetism's effect on light was unique. He tried electricity. Experiment after experiment failed. He died without ever having observed the effect of electricity on light. But later researchers, using far more sensitive apparatus, did see such effects.

For example, Faraday was convinced that a ray of polarized light passing through a decomposing electrolyte should show some effect of

Using a ray of polarized light, Faraday discovered
a link between light energy and magnetic force.

electricity. He thought, too, that light should be affected whenever and
wherever electrical lines of force existed. Thirty-two years later, another
Englishman, Dr. John Kerr, proved Faraday right.

The success of his experiments with magnetism and light convinced
Faraday more than ever that his magnetic lines of force were a reality.
Yet if they *were* real, Faraday wondered, why didn't they affect all matter? The only recognized effect of magnetism was to attract iron, cobalt,
nickel, and a few other substances.

Faraday began to look for a possible effect of magnetism on so-called
"nonmagnetic" materials. He soon found it. Again, he was helped by a
sample of the optical glass he had worked on many years before. Faraday revealed his new discovery in a letter to Auguste de la Rive:

"Now, if a square bar of this substance [Faraday's glass], about half
an inch thick and two inches long, be very freely suspended between the
poles of a powerful horse-shoe electro-magnet, immediately that the
magnetic force is developed, the bar points; but it does not point from
pole to pole, but equatorially or across the magnetic lines of force—i.e.,

47

east and west in respect of the north and south poles. If it be moved from this position it returns to it, and this continues as long as the magnetic force is in action."

Rapidly, Faraday tested a host of other materials; various kinds of liquids, solids, crystals, powders, acids, and oils. All acted exactly like his glass, setting themselves east-and-west across the magnetic lines of force. So did apples, bread, beef, and wax. He termed all these substances "diamagnetics" to distinguish them from ordinary magnetics. Faraday explained that diamagnetics tend to "move outwards" from the magnet, "or into positions of the weakest magnetic force."

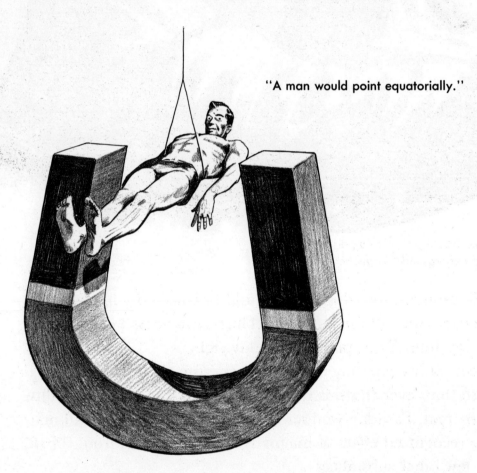

"A man would point equatorially."

Faraday wound up his study of diamagnetism with a rather remarkable thought. "If a man," he wrote, "could be suspended with sufficient delicacy . . . and placed in the magnetic field, he would point equatorially, for all the substances of which he is formed, including the blood, possess this property."

48   In his research on diamagnetism, Faraday had experimented with the magnetic properties of gases, and found that oxygen was strongly magnetic. This discovery resulted in one of the few faulty theories he ever held.

The magnetic nature of oxygen, Faraday proposed, fully accounted for so-called "magnetic storms" and other changes in the earth's magnetic field. He believed the oxygen in our atmosphere was always pushing and pulling the magnetic field out of kilter. Scientists now know that Faraday's explanation is inadequate. Atmospheric magnetism does affect the earth's magnetic field, as Faraday proved by long and careful experiment. But there are also other factors involved—such as cosmic rays and solar eruptions—which Faraday could not have known about or suspected.

Meanwhile, in 1846, Faraday had published a paper that rocked his scientific colleagues back on their heels. Even in 1868, a year after Faraday's death, his close friend and admirer John Tyndall felt called upon to apologize for it. Faraday, Tyndall implied, couldn't really have believed what he said in the paper, for it was "one of the most singular speculations that ever emanated from a scientific mind."

The paper suggested, simply and clearly, that light waves from the sun and stars were transmitted through the near-vacuum of space in vibrating lines of force. These lines of force were the same as the ones Faraday had been talking about, for years, in connection with magnetism and electricity.

This just couldn't be, said other scientists. According to accepted scientific beliefs, space was filled with a mysterious elastic fluid, known

"Magnetic storms," Faraday believed, were caused solely by the magnetic nature of oxygen in the Earth's atmosphere. Scientists now know that cosmic rays and solar eruptions are also to blame.

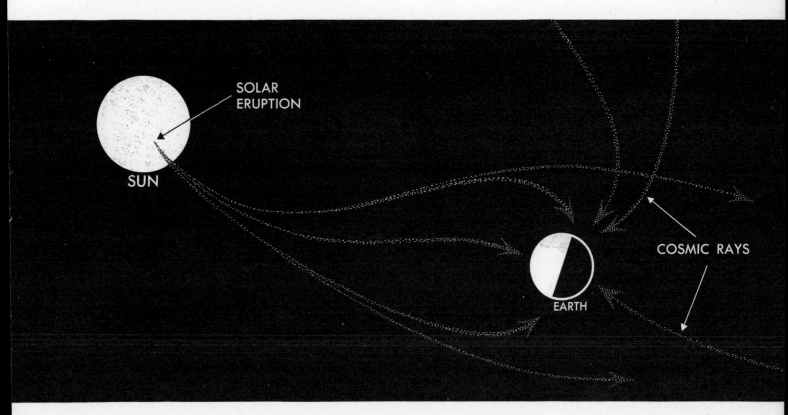

SOLAR
ERUPTION

SUN

EARTH

COSMIC RAYS

as "the luminiferous ether." It was the vibrations of this ether that enabled light to travel across space.

Faraday, however, had no use for the luminiferous ether. It smacked a little too much of his old enemy, "action at a distance." Besides, his lines of force could vibrate, too, much like a rubber cord stretched between two points. If such a cord is tweaked at one end, vibrations will travel along its whole length. Just so, the line of force carries the energy of light from its source to its destination.

Eighteen years after the paper appeared, the English mathematical physicist, James Clerk Maxwell, presented the world with mathematical evidence of the truth of Faraday's "most singular speculation." Although it became known as Maxwell's electromagnetic theory of light, Maxwell himself always gave full credit to Faraday for first stating it.

The theory continues to be a vital concept in modern physics, little changed from the form in which Faraday first conceived it. Light waves consist of magnetic and electrical energy, say modern physicists. This energy originates in some substance that has, somehow, become electrically charged. Thus, if he were alive today, Faraday could say about light what he had once said about chemical attraction: "Light is electricity, and electricity is light."

Untrained as a mathematician, Faraday never expressed his theories in mathematical symbols. Yet Maxwell was continually amazed by the unvarying mathematical accuracy of all Faraday's concepts of electromagnetism. So was the great German mathematical physicist, Hermann von Helmholtz, who wrote in 1881:

Maxwell stated Faraday's theory of light in mathematical terms.

Faraday met open criticism and ridicule in his attempts to prove gravity was a form of energy.

"Now that the mathematical interpretation of Faraday's conceptions regarding the nature of electric and magnetic forces has been given by Clerk Maxwell, we see how great a degree of exactness and precision was really hidden behind the words which to Faraday's contemporaries appeared either vague or obscure; and it is in the highest degree astonishing to see what a large number of general theorems, the methodical deduction of which requires the highest powers of mathematical analysis, he found by a kind of intuition, with the security of instinct, without the help of a single mathematical formula."

Faraday once humorously remarked that the only mathematical operation he had ever performed was turning the crank of an adding machine. He never lamented his lack of mathematical training. Experiment, to him, was a far more reliable scientific tool.

Of all Faraday's experiments, none were more ridiculed than his attempts to find a relationship between gravity and the other forces of nature. Many people felt that even the thought of such a relationship was absurd. To try to *prove* it by experiment, they felt, was sheer madness. Gravity was just too great and mysterious to ever submit to the tamperings of a scientist.

Faraday was well aware that his chances of success were exceedingly small, but he was determined to try anyway. "All this is a dream," he wrote in his notebook. "Still examine it by a few experiments. Nothing is too wonderful to be true, if it be consistent with the laws of nature, and in such things as these, experiment is the best test of such consistency."

He performed experiment after experiment in his laboratory at the Royal Institution, testing for gravity's effect on every form of energy. He took equipment to the top of the Clock Tower of the Houses of Parliament, to broaden the scale of his experiments. No results.

How could he find gravity's secret?
From the Clock Tower . . .?

But he kept at it. "It was almost with a feeling of awe that I went to work," wrote Faraday, "for if the hope [of gravitational effect] should prove well founded how great and mighty and sublime in its hitherto unchangeable character is the force I am trying to deal with, and how large may be the new domain of knowledge that may be opened up to the mind of man."

In 1860, Faraday sent a paper to the Royal Society on some possible relations he suspected between gravity and electricity. He was politely asked to take the paper back. The Royal Society wanted no more of Faraday's unprovable speculations.

When Faraday died seven years later, he had failed to prove any relationship between gravity and other forces. The idea was still regarded as rank speculation. Yet it is Faraday, after all, who may have the last word.

About fifty years later another great scientist, seeking proof for a theory of his own, predicted that a ray of light from a distant star, passing near the sun's rim on its way to earth, would be deflected slightly by the sun's gravitational field. When tested at various observatories during the solar eclipses of 1919 and 1922, this prediction proved true. The scientist was Albert Einstein, and the theory, relativity.

Thus Einstein found that gravity seems to influence the rays of light that stretch through space. He was working on a vast cosmic scale; Faraday in the comparatively tiny distances available in his laboratory and from the Clock Tower of the Houses of Parliament. But at the very least Einstein's discovery was a hint that Faraday's speculations about gravity may someday prove true.

Perhaps Faraday, too, suspected that the earth itself was too small a "laboratory" for his experiments. At one point he had written: "If there should be any truth in these vague expectations of the relation of the

Apparent Position
Of Star As Seen
From Earth Pos. 2

Actual
Position
Of Star

Bent By Sun's Gravity
Beam Of Starlight

Earth
Pos. 1

SUN

Earth
Pos. 2

Einstein extended Faraday's belief that
gravity was a form of energy like light.
Support for the belief came in 1920's.
Astronomers found star appears to change
position depending on whether Earth is on
near side of Sun (position no. 1) or far
54   side (position no. 2). Thus Sun's gravity
must bend ray of light energy (solid line).
We always see star as *if* its light trav-
eled straight (dotted line and below).

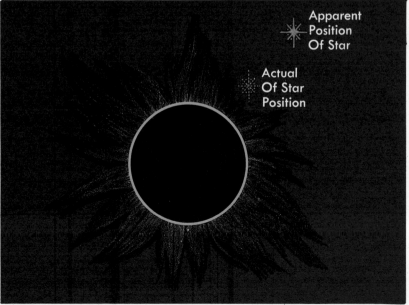

Apparent
Position
Of Star

Actual
Of Star
Position

Gravitating force, then it seems hardly possible but that there must be some extraordinary results to come out in relation to celestial mechanics —as between the earth and the moon, or the Sun and the planets, or in the great space between all gravitating bodies . . ."

Inevitably, Faraday's ideas led him to distrust one of the most cherished doctrines of nineteenth-century science. This was Dalton's atomic theory.

Through his belief in lines of force and the relationship of all forms of energy, Faraday had come to regard the universe as a vast, interconnected web of moving energy. In this view, the unbreakable, solid atoms of Dalton had no place. They were unwieldy and immovable boulders, where Faraday saw only graceful lines and curves of force, moving to and away from mere points. These points were not solid atoms, but merely "centers of force."

Faraday's distrust of the atomic theory was sternly criticized by other scientists of his day. His "centers of force" were thought to be vague, even meaningless concepts. But he clung stubbornly to the idea. In one of his last lectures, Faraday described every particle of matter as "a center of force, reaching to an infinite distance, binding worlds and suns together, and unchangeable in its permanency. Around this same particle," Faraday continued, "we see grouped the powers of all the various phenomena of nature: the heat, the cold, the wind, the storm, the awful conflagration, the vivid lightning flash, the stability of the rock and the mountain, the grand mobility of the ocean."

Now, as the modern physicists probe deeper and deeper into the heart of the atom, the distinction between matter and energy all but vanishes. Dalton's atoms divide and redivide into smaller and smaller particles. "What is matter if it is not also energy?" the physicist asks. "And where does energy dwell?"

In this light, Faraday's "centers of force" now grow in significance as Dalton's "unbreakable" atoms break and disappear.

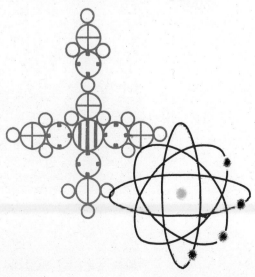

55

Index

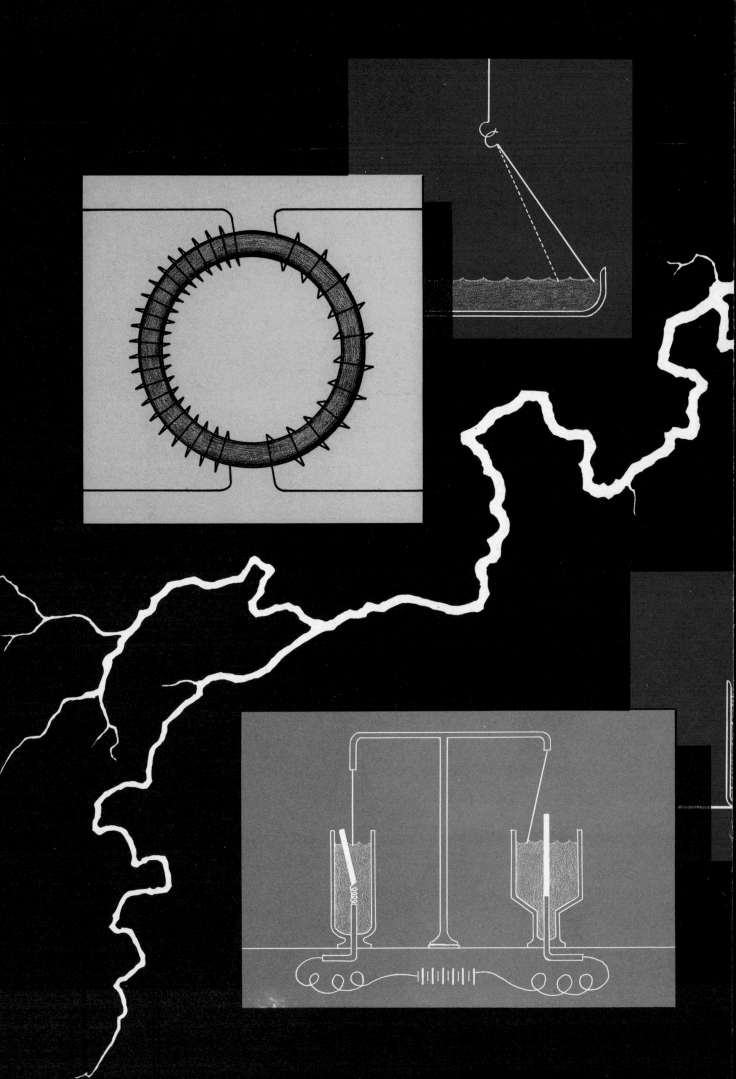